WOLVERINE

ORIGIN

WOLVERINE

PLOT
BILL JEMAS, JOE QUESADA & PAUL JENKINS

SCRIPT
PAUL JENKINS

PENCILER
ANDY KUBERT

DIGITAL PAINTER
RICHARD ISANOVE

LETTERERS
JOHN ROSHELL & COMICRAFT'S WES ABBOTT, OSCAR GONGORRA & SAIDA TEMOFONTE

COVER ART
JOE QUESADA & RICHARD ISANOVE

ASSISTANT EDITOR
MIKE RAICHT

EDITOR
MIKE MARTS

WOLVERINE: ORIGIN. Contains material originally published in magazine form as WOLVERINE: THE ORIGIN #1-6. Second edition. Fourth printing 2013. ISBN# 978-0-7851 3727-6. Published by MARVEL WORLDWIDE, INC., a subsidiary of MARVEL ENTERTAINMENT, LLC. OFFICE OF PUBLICATION: 135 West 50th Street, New York, NY 1002(Copyright © 2001, 2002 and 2009 Marvel Characters, Inc. All rights reserved. All characters featured in this issue and the distinctive names and likenesses thereof, and a related indicia are trademarks of Marvel Characters, Inc. No similarity between any of the names, characters, persons, and/or institutions in this magazine with those of an living or dead person or institution is intended, and any such similarity which may exist is purely coincidental. **Printed in the U.S.A.** ALAN FINE, EVP - Office of the Presiden Marvel Worldwide, Inc. and EVP & CMO Marvel Characters B.V.; DAN BUCKLEY, Publisher & President - Print, Animation & Digital Divisions; JOE QUESADA, Chief Creative Office TOM BREVOORT, SVP of Publishing; DAVID BOGART, SVP of Operations & Procurement, Publishing; C.B. CEBULSKI, SVP of Creator & Content Development; DAVID GABRIEL SVP of Print & Digital Publishing Sales; JIM O'KEEFE, VP of Operations & Logistics; DAN CARR, Executive Director of Publishing Technology; SUSAN CRESPI, Editorial Operation Manager; ALEX MORALES, Publishing Operations Manager; STAN LEE, Chairman Emeritus. For information regarding advertising in Marvel Comics or on Marvel.com, pleas contact Niza Disla, Director of Marvel Partnerships, at ndisla@marvel.com. For Marvel subscription inquiries, please call 800-217-9158. **Manufactured between 8/21/201** and 9/23/2013 by R.R. DONNELLEY, INC., SALEM, VA, USA.

10 9 8 7 6 5 4

COLLECTION EDITOR
MARK D. BEAZLEY

ASSISTANT EDITORS
NELSON RIBEIRO & ALEX STARBUCK

EDITOR, SPECIAL PROJECTS
JENNIFER GRÜNWALD

SENIOR EDITOR, SPECIAL PROJECTS
JEFF YOUNGQUIST

SVP OF PRINT & DIGITAL
PUBLISHING SALES
DAVID GABRIEL

BOOK DESIGNER
JEOF VITA

EDITOR IN CHIEF
AXEL ALONSO

CHIEF CREATIVE OFFICER
JOE QUESADA

PUBLISHER
DAN BUCKLEY

EXECUTIVE PRODUCER
ALAN FINE

SPECIAL THANKS TO RICHARD ISANOVE,
SPENCER BECK & CHRIS ALLO

ORIGIN

"What do you think of the idea of a limited series telling Wolverine's origin?"

Two words immediately popped into my head ... bad idea. That was how my first lunch with Joe Quesada began back in September of 2000. I had just spent the past four years of my life working to bring X-Men to life on the big screen and Wolverine was a big part of me. X-Men was the movie I wanted to make since I was twelve years old and I had assumed the role as the protector of the mythology on the film. But now it wasn't the studio system that was going to screw Logan up but Marvel itself. Nightmare visions of the Spider-Man "Clone Saga" danced through my head.

For the rest of the lunch Joe and I went back and forth debating the pros and cons of finally revealing the greatest mystery of comicdom — the history of Wolverine. I used all the arguments. That it would ruin the mystique of the character, that Logan wouldn't be as tragic a hero if we knew his past, even stooping to 'you should let the reader flesh out that mystery in their own head'. None of it worked. For as passionate as I was Joe was equally as passionate; and I could see in his eyes that he had already made up his mind, he was going to tell the origin of Logan. At that point I asked him "Why? Why take the chance of damaging the character?" Joe looked me dead in the eye and said, " If anyone is going to tell the origin of Logan, Marvel should do it first, not the movie." You know what? I agreed with him.

At that moment all of my fanboy trepidation turned into excitement, now I wanted to read it. Over eighteen months have passed since that lunch and I've been patiently waiting for all of the issues to come out so I could read ORIGIN at one sitting. I resisted the urge to read it every time a new issue came out, although I broke down and peeked at the artwork and was blown away by the lushness and sweep of the visuals, which owed more to Mark Twain than spandex-clad four color heroes. But I was going to wait. Two days ago I got a call saying that Bill Jemas and Joe Quesada wanted to know if I would write the foreward to the ORIGIN hardcover. Needless to say I feigned indifference and immediately asked if I could get copies of all the issues published and unpublished sent to me overnight. Of course FedEx was a day late. Well, having just finished reading ORIGIN, I think back on Joe's original question, "What do you think of the idea of a limited series telling Wolverine's origin?" and now what pops into my head is ... damn, I wish I had thought of that.

A True Believer Always,

Tom DeSanto
Executive Producer/ Co-Writer
X-Men: The Movie
2002

P.S. — To Messrs. Jenkins, Kubert, Isanove, Jemas, and Quesada: Success belongs to those who take the risk; thanks for taking the risk. But an even bigger thanks for succeeding.

PART ONE - THE HILL

"THAT THERE BUILDING IS THE *HOWLETT* ESTATE.

"THEY SAY IT WAS BUILT ON A FOUNDATION OF *TEARS.*"

I·I'M SORRY, MRS. HOPKINS, I'D BETTER GET ME THINGS...

BOTH OF 'EM ARE ·· HIM AN' THAT NO·GOOD FATHER A' 'IS, ALWAYS SCOWLIN' AT EVERYONE AND MISTREATIN' THE ANIMALS, I DUNNO WHY MASTER JOHN KEEPS 'IM ON.

YOU MARK MY WORDS, GIRL, THEY'RE A DIRTY BUNCH OF SCOUNDRELS, THEM LOGANS, THE BOY JUST AS MUCH AS 'IS FATHER.

MISTER LOGAN'S THE GROUNDSKEEPER UP HERE, YOU DON'T GO WITHIN FIFTY YARDS OF THAT MAN, UNDERSTAND?

NOW THEN, LET'S TAKE A LOOK AT YOU. YOU'LL BE MEETING MASTER JOHN IN A FEW MINUTES.

TCH...LOOK AT THE STATE OF YOU! YOU LOOK LIKE YOU WAS DRAGGED THROUGH A HEDGE BACKWARDS.

THIS IS A BIG OPPORTUNITY FOR A YOUNG GIRL, ROSE. ESPECIALLY SEEIN' AS HOW YOU CAN READ AN' WRITE AN' ALL.

I DONE YOU A GREAT FAVOR TO GET YOU AWAY FROM THE BOTTOM OF THE HILL, CHILD, SO DON'T YOU MESS IT UP...

...at the end of our day, James and I return to that sparkling, wonderful house on the hill...

...but poor Dog must always go back to his life down below.

MASTER JOHN, I SWEAR TO HEAVEN I DIDN'T KNOW HE WAS AT THE POND! I ONLY TURNED MY EYES FOR A MINUTE ··

OHH, SIR! ӠAh·hehӠ ... IF ONLY I'D SEEN 'IM RUN *OFF* ··

HUSH, ROSE... DON'T CONCERN YOURSELF SO, YOU'RE GETTING WETTER THAN THESE TWO SCALLYWAGS.

DON'T WORRY ABOUT ANY RAMIFICATIONS, LOGAN, LET'S JUST BE RELIEVED EVERYONE'S INTACT, SHALL WE? "BOYS WILL BE BOYS," AFTER ALL.

HERE, CHILD... DRY YOURSELF WITH THIS ··

WHAT? YOU'RE LETTING THEM GO WITHOUT *PUNISHMENT?* IN MY DAY, THE BOY WOULD HAVE BEEN FLOGGED, AS WOULD HIS *FATHER*, IN MY DAY ··

THIS ISN'T YOUR DAY, PAPA.

THOMAS, I WANT YOU TO TAKE YOUR BOY HOME AND TAKE CARE OF HIM, UNDERSTOOD?

OH, I *WILL*, SIR.

Christmas has been such a lovely season, dear diary. James received a special gift from his father: a sweet little puppy! I can't tell you how excited he was!

Today, it was Boxing Day. Master John was so funny about it... and so kind! He served up honey punch, dressed in one of Mrs. Hopkins' aprons! How the servants laughed!

WHAT **NONSENSE**, JOHN. WHERE'S THE DECORUM IN ACTING LIKE A FOOL IN FRONT OF THE SERVANTS...?

PAPA, JUST FOR ONE DAY I'M NOT GOING TO ALLOW YOU TO SPOIL MY FUN. IT'S BOXING DAY, AND I RATHER **LIKE** THE TRADITION OF SERVING THE HELP FOR ONE AFTERNOON.

NOW, IF YOU'LL EXCUSE ME, I HAVE TO GO AND WISH SOMEONE A MERRY CHRISTMAS...

HELLO, ROSE, WHY SO GLUM?

OH, SIR... *SNIFF* I'M AWFUL SORRY, IT'S JUST...

... I MISS ME MAM AN' DAD SO MUCH. MAM'D ALWAYS MAKE ME A PRETTY NEW DRESS AT CHRISTMAS...

YES, WELL... THAT'S A SHAME. NOW, I REALLY MUST GET BACK TO THE PARTY...

MASTER JOHN, SIR! THE BOY WAS *SPYING* IN THE WINDOW!

OH, FOR GOODNESS SAKE, KENNETH, LET THE BOY GO, HE'S DONE NO HARM.

YOU'RE LOGAN'S BOY, AREN'T YOU? WE HAVEN'T SEEN YOU AROUND HERE MUCH LATELY ··

I·I'M SORRY, MASTER JOHN, SIR, HONEST.

HERE... JAMES IS BUSY WITH HIS NEW PUPPY ·· I DOUBT HE'LL MISS ONE MORE TOY. WHAT DO YOU SAY?

OH, *THANK* YOU, SIR! MERRY CHRISTMAS, SIR!

GOOD BOY, NOW BE OFF WITH YOU ··

THIS IS THE *FINAL STRAW*, JOHN! ARE YOU GOING TO HAND THEM THE KEYS TO THE *SAFE* NEXT? I WON'T STAND FOR IT!

WHAT DO YOU MEAN, YOU WON'T STAND FOR IT? THIS IS *MY* HOUSE, FATHER ··

YES, AND BUILT ON THE STRENGTH OF *MY* MONEY!

YOUR MONEY? AH, SO IT RETURNS TO YOU EACH AND EVERY TIME YOU FIND *DISPLEASURE* WITH ME, DOES IT?

HOW *DARE* YOU TALK TO YOUR FATHER THAT WAY!

POPPA! *POPPA!*
OOK WHAT MASTER
HOWLETT ..

.. GAVE
ME.

PART II - INNER CHILD

I always knew that Logan boy would be trouble.

If you ask my opinion, James is *never* going to be fine — not with the way his grandfather pressures him. I don't know how Master John has the patience to speak civilly to the old goat.

An unutterable sadness fills the air in the house nowadays. Everything seems so much *more* — the Old Man seems more impatient, poor Master John seems more weary.

It's only James who seems less than before. He's as pale as a ghost and weaker than a kitten thanks to his allergies.

He coughs and sulks and suffers from morning till night. If it weren't for that dog of his that he loves so much, I'm sure he'd already have gone the way of his brother.

How insufferably tragic we've all become, dear diary! I fear this house is going to be the death of us *all*.

KNOCK KNOCK

I WASN'T NEEDED DOWNSTAIRS, MA'AM ‥

AAH!

WHAT'S *SHE* DOING HERE? GET HER *OUT!*

YOU WERE SUPPOSED TO *KNOCK*, GIRL! GET OUT OF HERE *AT ONCE* ‥

I·I'M SORRY... I *FORGOT.*

NOT A WORD, YOUNG ROSE ‥ YOU *HEAR* ME?

NOT A *WORD.*

... Hhh...
⅀Ah·Hehh...⅀   Ohhh...

Oh, LORD...
Oh DEAR LORD...
⅀snff...⅀

'LO,
ROSE.

I FIGURED
YA'D MAKE IT OUT
T' SEE ME BEFORE
LONG. I BEEN WAITIN'
FER YA, AS IF YA
DIDN'T KNOW.

I... I
HAVE TO
LEAVE,
DOG ··

WHY NOT
STAY A
WHILE?

DON'T BE SHY,
ROSE. IT'S TIME WE GOT T'
KNOW EACH OTHER, YOU
AND ME ··

NNN... STOP
IT, DOG! YOU'RE
HURTING ME!

ROSE ··?

DON'T SAY I DIDN'T *WARN* YOU, LOGAN·· I GAVE YOU EVERY CHANCE TO DISCIPLINE THE BOY. HAD YOU BEEN A *SUITABLE* PARENT, THIS WOULD HAVE NEVER HAPPENED.

MY SON'S BESIDE HIMSELF WITH *GRIEF* AS A RESULT OF YOUR BOY'S ACTIONS. YOU MAY COUNT ON ME BEING A MAN OF MY *WORD*·· I HOLD YOU RESPONSIBLE FOR THIS, AS PROMISED.

I EXPECT YOU OFF MY PROPERTY WITHIN THE *HOUR*··

DON'T YOU TALK T' ME LIKE *THAT*, HOWLETT! I SEEN THE WAY Y' ACT AROUND US... YOU THINK YE'RE *BETTER* THAN US!

YA CAN'T *DO* THIS TO ME! I'LL HAVE YOUR BLOODY *HIDE*··

I WON'T *HAVE* YOUR INSOLENCE, DO YOU *HEAR ME*, LOGAN? AFTER THIS, BE THANKFUL I DON'T HAVE YOU BOTH *HUNG!*

NOW, GET THIS MAN OUT OF MY *SIGHT.*

I **TOLD** YOU THIS WOULD HAPPEN, JOHN! I WARNED YOU NOT TO ASSOCIATE WITH THOSE PEOPLE·· NO GOOD WOULD COME OF IT, I SAID, WE'RE BEYOND THEIR **STATION** IN LIFE··

≡Huff···≡ C'MON NOW, THOMAS, DON'T MAKE THIS ANY HARDER··

YOU CAN'T **DO** THIS TO ME, YOU BASTARDS! LET **GO** OF ME!

I'M **WARNIN'** YOU! GET YOUR FILTHY MITTS OFFA ME··

YOU SHOULDN'T HAVE SPOKEN T' MASTER JOHN LIKE THAT, LOGAN. IF YOU KNOW WHAT'S BEST, YE'LL NOT COME BACK HERE AGAIN, HEAR?

Uhf··!

I'LL GET YOU, **HEAR** ME? THE WHOLE LOT O' YOU!

I'LL MAKE YOU **PAY!**

RrrTrr...

SLAM

I NEVER *MEANT* IT, POPPA! I *SWEAR!* IT WAS ALL *HIS* FAULT!

PLEASE, POPPA... DON'T KILL ME. I SWEAR, I WAS JUST DOIN' WHAT YOU SAID...

I KNOW, BOY, IT WASN'T YOUR FAULT ·· IT WAS SOFT JOHN AN' THAT SOFT FOOL BOY O' HIS WHAT DONE THIS TO US.

A MAN LIKE THAT DON'T *DESERVE* HIS PLACE IN LIFE·· NOT WITH THAT FINE HOUSE AN' FINE *WOMAN* O' HIS.

I SAY IT'S TIME WE MADE A *CHANGE* TO THAT.

♪ ...AND WISH THAT HE COULD STA-AY... MY BONNIE LAD FROM FAR A-WAAAY...

''Mmf.

NOT A *SOUND*, ELIZABETH. IT'S ME... THOMAS. UNDERSTAND?

Mm-hmm.

WE'RE GETTING OUT OF HERE, AN' I'M TAKIN' YOU *WITH* ME, TONIGHT.

WHERE'S THE MONEY?

I COULDN'T HELP IT, MA'AM, THEY *MADE* ME DO IT.

THOMAS, ARE YOU UTTERLY *MAD* COMING HERE LIKE THIS? LET THE GIRL *GO*-'

NO! SHE'S COMIN' WITH US!

ELIZABETH? WHAT'S *GOING ON* IN HERE!

PART III - THE BEAST WITHIN

I will remember that sound until the day I die.

It was an awful, revolting noise ~ not a scream, but the birth-cry of a new creature that surely had no place on God's earth.

The thing mewled and whimpered in pain, and those of us who could stand in witness were transfixed ~ both repelled and fascinated by the grotesque spectacle of it.

NN·AHWW... PAPA!

Oh, DEAR GOD.

AWHH... UHH...

AAH! MY HANDS! MY HANDS!

NOK NOK

ENOUGH! WHOEVER THE BLAZES YOU ARE, I'M NOT *DEAF* ··

MISTER HOWLETT, SIR, THESE GENTLEMEN ARE FROM THE LOCAL CONSTABULARY. THEY'RE, um... HERE ON A MATTER OF *URGENCY*.

AND *SO*? WHAT COULD BE SO *URGENT* THAT YOU'D ROUSE A MAN AT THIS UNGODLY HOUR?

WELL? SPIT IT *OUT*, MAN ··

THERE'S BEEN AN INCIDENT UP AT THE *HOUSE*, SIR.

IT INVOLVES YOUR SON AND HIS FAMILY.

JAMES... I'M SO SORRY -- I DON'T KNOW WHAT TO *DO*. I'M AFRAID TO GO BACK TO THE HOUSE! WHAT IF THEY THINK IT WAS *ME*?

OH, LORD... *=SNFF=*... I DON'T KNOW WHAT I'M GOING TO *DO*! I DON'T EVEN KNOW IF THIS IS *REAL*, WHAT'S *HAPPENED* TO YOU?

DO... DO I *KNOW* YOU?

JAMES, YOU'RE COLD...

I HAVE A FIREPLACE AT MY HOME. IT'S NOT FAR. WE CAN GO THERE.

JAMES, WE CAN'T GO BACK TO THE HOUSE ·· NOT UNTIL I KNOW WHAT TO DO.

OH, LORD! LOOK AT YOUR HANDS!

THEM THINGS... THEY'RE GOING BACK INSIDE, ARE YOU MAKING 'EM DO THAT?

I DON'T KNOW ... I THINK I'VE BEEN UNWELL AGAIN, ROSE.

CAN WE GO TO WHERE IT'S WARM NOW?

I DON'T THINK WE HAVE ANY CHOICE, JAMES.

WHO THE DEVIL'S THERE? **SHOW** YOURSELF!

SNAP

SO, IT'S **YOU!** NO DOUBT COME TO FINISH THE **JOB**, HAVE YOU, YOU MURDEROUS LITTLE WENCH?

SIR, I HAD **NOTHING** TO DO WITH IT, I **SWEAR!** IT WAS MISTER LOGAN WHAT FORCED HIS WAY INTO THE HOUSE!

SOMETHIN'S HAPPENED TO MASTER JAMES, HIS **HANDS** ··

SHUT UP, GIRL, AND **LISTEN** TO ME.

IF YOU WISH TO **LIVE**, YOU'RE GOING TO DO **EXACTLY** AS I SAY.

OH, SIR... I PROMISE HE'LL DO HIS SHIFT. HE'LL DO *MORE* THAN HIS SHIFT!

YOU JUST HAVE TO LET US *STAY* FOR A WHILE ··

WE'LL *SEE* ABOUT THAT, LASS. WHAT'S HIS NAME?

I DON'T WANT YOUR LIFE STORY, GIRL. I'M NOT INTERESTED IN WHERE YOU CAME FROM OR WHAT YOU'RE RUNNING FROM.

I JUST NEED A *NAME* FOR HIM, THAT'S ALL.

WELL?

LOGAN, SIR.

HIS NAME IS *LOGAN.*

PART IV - HEAVEN AND HELL

WHERE THE DEVIL YOU **BEEN**, BOY? WE GOT ANOTHER FIFTY BARROWS TO GET THROUGH BEFORE DAY'S END!

I·I'M SORRY, SMITTY··

SORRY DON'T CUT IT HERE, BUB, THIS PLACE, YOU SHAPE UP QUICK, OR YOU **DIE**, THERE AIN'T NO FREE RIDES, 'CAUSE I **SAY** THERE AIN'T.

NOW GET THIS LOAD DOWN THE HILL AN' BE BACK UP HERE IN SEVEN MINUTES··

··· AH·HEHH··· ≡SNIFF≡···

THANKS.

HEY, THE PLEASURE'S *MINE* ·· THAT'S WHAT FRIENDS ARE *FOR*, RIGHT?

PEOPLE LIKE YOU AN' ME, WE GOTTA *STICK TOGETHER*, WE GOTTA HELP EACH OTHER OUT ··

·· OOPS.

NO! **NO!**

AH·HUHH...

JAMES..?

SLAM

JAMES, ARE YOU ALL RIGHT? WHAT'S HAPPENED?

NOTHING.

Oh, JAMES... I'M SO SORRY FOR BRINGING YOU HERE.. I JUST DIDN'T KNOW WHERE ELSE TO GO.

BUT WE HAVE TO BE *CAREFUL* FOR A WHILE, OKAY? WE HAVE TO MAKE SURE NO ONE KNOWS WHO WE ARE... WE CAN'T GET INVOLVED.

YOU CAN TELL ME WHAT IT IS, JAMES.. I *PROMISE.*

IS THERE SOMETHING YOU WANT TO SAY?

NO.

We're now into our second summer at the camp, dear diary "" There's a thick curtain of leaves on the trees now, but I fancy even the forest can't disguise the squalor of this awful place.

I can't help thinking how angry Mother Nature must be that she can't cover such an ugly stain on her pretty dress.

I'm not sure I even remember what the world outside the camp looks like anymore. I sometimes feel as though everything has changed "" no one more so than James.

Did it really all happen, I wonder? Or was it just a dream?

AAH!

I CAN *HEAR* YOU BACK THERE ·· I KNOW YOU'RE *SPYING* ON ME! WHO'S TH··

SNAP

·· OH, LORD...

"THE FEAST" BY RICHARD ISANOVE

PART V - REVELATION

"*TYGER! TYGER! BURNING BRIGHT IN THE FORESTS OF THE NIGHT, WHAT IMMORTAL HAND OR EYE COULD FRAME THY FEARFUL SYMMETRY?*"

CRISH

"*IN WHAT DISTANT DEEPS OR SKIES BURNT THE FIRE OF THINE EYES?*"

"*ON WHAT WINGS DARE HE ASPIRE? WHAT THE HAND DARE SEIZE THE FIRE?*"

CROOSH

KRIK

"*AND WHAT SHOULDER, AND WHAT ART, COULD TWIST THE SINEWS OF THY HEART, AND WHEN THY HEART BEGAN TO BEAT...*"

"*...WHAT DREAD HAND? AND WHAT DREAD FEET?*"

"DID HE WHO MADE THE LAMB MAKE THEE?"

WHEN THE STARS THREW DOWN THEIR SPEARS, AND WATER'D HEAVEN WITH THEIR TEARS, DID HE SMILE HIS WORK TO SEE?

TYGER! TYGER! BURNING BRIGHT, IN THE FORESTS OF THE NIGHT, WHAT IMMORTAL HAND OR EYE...

"...DARE FRAME THY FEARFUL SYMMETRY?"

≡Ah·HEM≡... HELLO, LAD, ME AN' YOUR COUSIN WERE JUST VISITIN' FOR A WHILE TILL YOU CAME BY.

*SHIFT FOREMAN TELLS ME YOUR CREW FINISHED OVER **QUOTA** AGAIN, I WANTED TO TALK TO YOU ABOUT THAT ··*

*SO **TALK.***

LOGAN, MISTER SMITH'S BEEN KIND ENOUGH TO BRING BY SOME BOOKS HE PICKED UP FROM HIS DAYS AT SEA. ISN'T THAT KIND OF HIM?

*AYE, WELL, LOOK... I **REALLY** CAME BY T' SEE **YOU,** LAD, CLEAN YOURSELF UP AN' GET SOME REST TONIGHT.*

I'LL WANT YOU TO TAKE THE MORNIN' OFF TOMORROW AN' COME MEET ME UP ON THE HILL, BY THE NEW SEAM.

*WHAT **FOR?***

*I GOT A **JOB** FOR YOU.*

UP YOU COME, LAD. I GOT A LITTLE SURPRISE FER YOU ··

I TAKE IT YOU HEARD ABOUT RODDY FINNEGAN? BLEW HIS BLEEDIN' *FINGERS* OFF LAST WEEK, THE DAFT OLD SOD.

SINCE HE'S GONE BLIND, I'LL NEED TO TRAIN SOMEONE WITH MORE THAN TWO OUNCES OF SENSE TO WORK THE DYNAMITE, I FIGURED IT'D BE *YOU*, IF YOU SHAPE UP.

IT AIN'T TOO HARD, BUT MOST OF MY LADS AIN'T GOT ENOUGH SMARTS TO BE CAREFUL ENOUGH. IT'S A HIGHLY MISUNDERSTOOD EXPLOSIVE, IS DYNAMITE.

SEE? YOU PLACE IT LIKE THIS ·· FUSE UP, IF YOU CAN. YOU FIND A SEAM AND THE BLAST LETS THE WEIGHT DO THE REST.

OKAY... I GOT IT. HOW LONG'RE THE *FUSES?*

EXACTLY ONE MINUTE!

HAW! TWO PAIR!

AGAIN? THERE AIN'T NO ONE COULD BE THAT LUCKY··

WHAT, YOU TRYIN' TO SAY I'M CHEATIN', COOKIE? I'LL HAVE YOUR GUTS FOR GARTERS!

I DIDN'T MEAN IT, FRED·· YOU KNOW THAT, I WAS JUST SAYIN' ··

YEAH? WELL, YOU BETTER UN·SAY IT.

HEY, AIN'T THAT THE LOGAN KID WITH SMITTY?

TELL YOU WHAT, COOKIE·· THAT KID TURNED OUT TO BE ALL RIGHT, A HARD WORKER, THAT ONE IS. BEST I EVER SEEN WITH A SHOVEL.

HE'S A DIGGER, ALL RIGHT, HE'S LIKE··· YOU EVER SEEN ONE OF THEM WOLVERINES GOIN' AFTER A ROOT? THEY NEVER GIVE UP TILL THEY GOT IT.

THAT'S WHAT THAT KID IS·· HE'S A WOLVERINE.

YOU LITTLE RUNT ·· YOU COME HERE OUT OF THE BLUE BLOODY SKY AN' STEAL AWAY MY MATES.

SO, SMITTY SAYS YOU'RE GONNA HANDLE ALL THE *CHARGES* FROM NOW ON, ARE YOU? WELL, LET'S SEE YOU HANDLE *THIS* ··

SNIP

THERE, SEE? IF YOU LOOK AT THE BOTTOM LINE ON THE LEDGER, IT SAYS WE'RE TURNIN' A BETTER PROFIT NOW THAN AT ANY TIME SINCE YOU TOOK OVER.

I'LL TELL YOU SOMETHIN', LASS ·· YOU BEEN NOTHIN' BUT A GODSEND TO THIS QUARRY, THAT'S THE BEST NEWS I HAD ALL *YEAR* ··

WHY, THANK YOU, GOOD SIR! Hehh...

SMITTY! *SMITTY!*

Tch, HONEST TO GOD, NOBBY, YOU OLD WASHER· WOMAN, WHAT IS IT *THIS* TIME?

UP AT THE ROCK FACE! THERE'S BEEN A *CAVE·IN!*

SSSSSSSHHH KOOM

SMITTY! YOU GOTTA COME BACK DOWN FER A WHILE! TAKE A REST! YOU AIN'T GONNA BE NO GOOD TO ANYONE SOAKED HALF' T' DEATH OUT HERE!

YOU SEE THEM OVER THERE? THAT'S FIVE GOOD MEN I LOST TODAY, AN' I AIN'T STOPPIN' TILL I FIND THE REST WHO'S MISSIN', I GOT A PROMISE TO KEEP··

C'MON, SMITTY·· THIS IS BLOODY USELESS, AN' YOU KNOW IT. SOON AS THAT SEAM WENT, THEM POOR BUGGERS WERE GONERS··

NO! I AIN'T LOSIN' ANY MORE OF MY MEN, YOU HEAR ME?

YOU ALREADY LOST 'EM, SMITTY!

...DAMNDEST THING I EVER SAW. YOU DON'T NEED *ME* TO TELL YOU THAT WAS SOME KIND O' *MIRACLE* OUT THERE LAST NIGHT, LOGAN.

MATTHEW FOWLER'S WIFE LOST HER HUSBAND IN THE SLIDE. SHE WANTED ME TO THANK YOU THAT SHE DIDN'T LOSE HER *SON*, AS WELL.

HERE YOU GO, LAD... THIS IS FOR YOU ··

WHAT IS IT?

MORE OF THEM OLD BOOKS OF MINE ·· SOMETHIN' TO PASS THE TIME WHILE YOU MEND UP. I BROUGHT THIS ONE BACK FROM NAGASAKI, JAPAN.

IT'S A MANUSCRIPT ABOUT *SAMURAI* FIGHTERS FROM THE OLD DAYS, I'LL TELL YOU... THEM LITTLE JAPANESE SCOUNDRELS ARE PRETTY SWIFT ·· I SEEN ONE OF 'EM BRING DOWN A TREE TRUNK WITH HIS BARE FISTS.

MATTER OF FACT, I LEARNED A LOT FROM THEM... ABOUT THE WORLD AN' ABOUT LIFE. IT'S A STRONG PERSON WHO FOLLOWS HIS OWN PATH, THEY SAY. I SEE THAT STRENGTH IN *YOU*, LOGAN.

YOU SHOULD HAVE *DIED* LAST NIGHT. I DON'T KNOW HOW YOU SAVED THAT BOY, AN' I AIN'T GONNA *PRY*, BUT WHATEVER IT *IS* ABOUT YOU, SON, YOU NEED T' KNOW IT DON'T MAKE NO DIFFERENCE TO ME ONE WAY OR THE OTHER, UNDERSTAND?

ANYWAY, I GOTTA GET BACK T' THE QUARRY.

MISS ROSE ·· CAN I ASK YOU TO WALK WITH ME FOR A FEW MINUTES?

≡HMMF≡ WELL, WHAT'S THIS THEN ·· *SILVER* ·· IS IT?

FIND ANYTHIN' YOU *LIKE,* BUB?

YOU'RE A *MONSTER,* COOKIE. FIVE MEN ARE DEAD, AN' WHILE EVERYONE'S DOWN AT THE FUNERALS, YOU'RE DIGGIN' THROUGH THEIR LIFELONG POSSESSIONS FER SCRAPS ··

JUST BREATHE A WORD OF THIS, KNUCKLEHEAD, AN' YOU'LL BE THE *NEXT* FUNERAL.

THERE AIN'T NO ONE GONNA BELIEVE YOUR WORD OVER *MINE.* I'LL SHUT YOUR MOUTH FER GOOD ··

·· HH· UHH!

CRUNCH

AAH!

YIPE

...Hhh...
UHH...

WHINE

PART VI - DUST TO DUST

HOWLETT, HUH?

LET'S JUST SAY I *DID*.. KNOW SOMETHING.. WHAT WOULD THAT INFORMATION BE *WORTH* TO YOU?

I NEED TO FIND HIM, IT'S *IMPORTANT*.

OWES YOU MONEY, HUH? WELL, I DON'T KNOW NO HOWLETT, BUT YOU COULD TRY THE QUARRY DOWN ABOUT TWO MILES SOUTH.

THERE'S A FELLER KINDA LIKE YOU'RE DESCRIBING, BUT CALLS HIMSELF *LOGAN*, CAME IN A FEW YEARS BACK WITH A *REDHEAD*..

EGKKK''E

THANKS.

LOGAN!

LOGAN, THIS BUSINESS HAS GONE ON *LONG ENOUGH.*

AREN'T YOU GOING TO TELL ME WHAT'S *BOTHERING* YOU?

I ALWAYS THOUGHT WE'D BE *TOGETHER,* ROSE, I MEAN... I ALWAYS HOPED...

...WON'T YOU *STAY* WITH ME?

I... I *CAN'T.*

...SO ANYWAY, TED, I FIGURED SINCE YOU WERE ALWAYS LATE FOR YOUR SHIFT MAYBE YOU COULD *USE* A GOOD WATCH. THIS HERE'S A PIECE OF TRUE QUALITY·· PICKED IT UP IN SWITZERLAND··

Mmf. I CAN'T EVEN *TELL TIME*, SMITTY.

... FOUR PLACES LEFT OPEN, LADS! THIS IS YOUR LAST CHANCE FOR TWO HUNDRED DOLLARS!

...JUST SIGN UP AT THE BOARD. FIGHTIN' BEGINS IN AN HOUR·· WINNER TAKES ALL!

YOU THINKIN' OF GETTIN' IN, FRIEND?

YEAH, SOMETHIN' LIKE THAT.

I GOTTA GET SOME CASH FOR THE TRAIN. ME AND MY GIRL ARE GOING TO THE CITY TONIGHT·· I'M GETTIN' HER *OUT* OF THIS SLAG HEAP··

Oh, YEAH? WHAT'S HER *NAME*, THIS GIRL OF YOURS?

PRETTIEST GIRL IN ALL OF CANADA, SHE IS, HER NAME'S *ROSE.*

REALLY?

'SCUSE ME, STRANGER·· I GOT SOME BUSINESS ON THE FLOOR.

GO RIGHT AHEAD.

LOGAN, MY BOY! YER COUSIN ROSE TOLD ME IF I SAW YOU, YOU WERE TO COME UP BY THE CABIN BEFORE WE LEAVE FOR VANCOUVER.

LOGAN?

HEY, LADS·· IT'S "LITTLE SMITTY!"

NO, IT AIN'T, AN' DON'T EVER CALL ME THAT AGAIN.

YOU GONNA SIGN UP FOR THE CAGE FIGHTS, LOGAN? THEY'RE GIVIN' OUT A CASH PRIZE··

I DUNNO...

CONSIDER THAT *PAYBACK* FOR HUMILIATING ME, YOU LITTLE PIECE OF COW DUNG. YOU WANT SOME MORE OF OL' COOKIE?

UHH... NICE SHOT, COOKIE, YOU FAT APE. LET'S SEE IF YOU CAN DO IT *TWICE*.

ARRGH!

VOLVERINE! WOLVERINE! WOLVERINE! WOLVERINE! WOLVER...

C'MON, LOGAN! PULL HIS *NACKERS* OFF!

WOLVERINE! WOLVERINE!

GAAH!

Hr-AHHH!!

WOLVERINE! WOLVERINE! WOLVERINE!

AUHH!

HOLY··

AN' THE WINNAH BY KNOCKOUT... *SMITTY!*

"...I CAN'T BELIEVE SMITTY DID THAT..."

"...I WAS *SURE* HE HAD 'IM DOWN..."

"...LIKE HE TOOK A *DIVE,* OR SOMETHIN'..."

YOU OKAY, BUB?

I'LL ALWAYS LOVE HER, SMITTY, I WANT YOU TO KNOW THAT.

IF YOU EVER HURT HER IN ANY WAY, I'LL COME LOOKIN' FOR YOU.

LOGAN, I NEED A FAVOR...

... I'VE RECOMMENDED TO THE BOSSES THAT YOU TAKE OVER AS FOREMAN. THE MINE AN' ALL THE BOYS ARE YOURS NOW·· MAKE SURE YOU TREAT THEM WELL, OKAY?

JUST GET OUT OF HERE BEFORE I CHANGE MY MIND, AN' TAKE CARE OF MY ROSE, YOU HEAR?

SURE THING, KID, YOU LOOK AFTER YOURSELF··

YOU *TOO*, BUB.

HEY! HOWLETT!

JAMES HOWLETT!

YOU STOLE MY NAME!

MY **MOM...?**
BUT I DON'T...
I MEAN...

Oh, LORD.

ALL COMIN' **BACK** TO YOU, EH?
'COURSE, YOU WEREN'T
THERE WHEN SHE BLEW HER **BRAINS
OUT**·· RIGHT IN FRONT
OF EVERYONE.

YOU WERE TOO BUSY
RUNNING AWAY WITH
THAT **IRISH WHORE,**
I TOLD THAT LITTLE
STRUMPET SHE
SHOULDA STAYED
WITH ME.

LOGAN!
NO!

HELLO,
ROSE.

Oh MY GOD...
DOG!

I'LL CATCH
UP WITH YOU
SOON, GIRL...

WHACK

...FIRST I GOTTA SEE IF LITTLE
JAMES REMEMBERS HOW I
WAS THE ONE WHO KILLED
HIS **POPPA!**
AND YOU
TWO GOT TH'
BLAME··

NO...

END

This all started in the basement of Joe Quesada's house in New Jersey.

Joe had just taken on the Chief job and invited his editors to an all-day creative session. Paul Jenkins had flown up from Atlanta to help out. (Paul and Joe had done some great work together in recent years, including THE INHUMANS and THE SENTRY.)

I showed up in the middle of the morning with the meeting already in progress. Joe was standing in front of his new staff with a clipboard and markers, and he was dying up there. Nobody had any ideas for their new boss.

This group of editors was, and is, the best in the business. These were the same men and women who would turn Marvel (and the comics industry) around during the next 18 months. But that morning, they were a quiet bunch. To be fair, and to make a long story short, this team had stuck with Marvel through thick and thin. The thin was the Bankruptcy, when Marvel employees had to survive the deepest depression in the history of the comics market and the tender mercies of Carl Icahn. Conditions like that make you learn to keep your head low, so when Joe asked for hot new ideas, he got a lot of cold blank stares and SECRET WARS III, and INFINITY GAUNTLET IV. This was a very uncomfortable scene and way, way too embarrassing to watch.

So I sat in the corner with Paul, eating donuts, when it hit me . . . I turned to Paul, "What is the greatest story Marvel never told?" He didn't miss a beat: "The Origin of Wolverine." Of course, we're sure we're geniuses, and we're about to spring this on everybody when Joe calls for the lunch break.

Paul and I were so full of sugar and oil that we couldn't eat lunch. We tracked down Joe, who was sitting with an editor munching on a burger. Paul asked Joe, "What is the greatest story Marvel never told?" Joe didn't miss a beat. "The Origin of Wolverine", but then he blurted out "But we could never tell it." The editor patiently explained to Paul and me that our brilliant and original idea had come up (and had been shot down) in every brainstorm session since Wolverine made his spectacular and mysterious first appearance in INCREDIBLE HULK #181. Joe added that revealing the Origin of Wolverine would ruin the character.

Now it's time for fun with Joey. We can't print exactly what I said to Joe, but the gist was "When we named you Editor in Chief, we thought we were passing the torch that lights the House of Ideas. I didn't think I was handing you a big chicken suit." Anyway, Joe got jolted back to being Joe, and got excited enough to blast out forty great marketing ideas in the following four minutes.

Joe started the afternoon session with a challenge to his team, "Bill Jemas wants us to tell the Origin of Wolverine. Bill says this will be the best-selling book in the entire industry in 2001. What should we tell him?"

As a group, the editors politely, but firmly, told me, "no way." Over the next hour, they explained that the essence of Logan is the search for his past; take that away and you destroy the Wolverine character. Destroy Wolverine, the most important X-Men character, and you destroy the X-Men. Destroy the X-Men, the most important Marvel family, and you destroy Marvel.

The bottom line was that Marvel was afraid. We were afraid to tell the story of the most courageous character in our Universe.

Then something interesting happened; the senior editors, Tom Brevoort, Ralph Macchio and Mark Powers started thinking and talking like senior editors. I believe it was Tom who stood up and said, "If we can tell a great story, we should go ahead and tell it. That's what we do."

That whole afternoon, I had the ideas that you are about to read in the following outline swirling around in my brain. I thought that the policy discussion was much more important than a bull session on my little springboard. More importantly, we had to do this right. Some of the best creators in the world work for Marvel and on the X-Men; those people deserved the first shot at writing Origin.

Let's fast-forward over the next several months. Joe kept asking for Origin pitches from the top talent in the industry, and kept getting turned down. He was offering the keys to the Jag, and nobody wanted to drive. Finally, Joe went back to Paul. Paul turned in a pretty fair pitch, but we all (Paul, too) agreed that it wasn't the right way to go.

Now it's March 2001, and we really needed to get this thing started. I went home and sat with my two sons – they were six and nine at the time – and we talked about what Logan would have been like as a kid. What kind of childhood could make a kid grow up as tough as Wolverine on the outside and give him a heart of gold on the inside?

This kind…

Bill Jemas

Bill Jemas

Former President & COO
Publishing, Consumer Products and
New Media
2002

PART ONE - TEXAS –
SET IN DALLAS SUBURB

TEXAS CHARACTERS

Dawg: Middle-school bully – nasty brutish and short.
• Wolverine junior, but this kid is all beast and no heart. Terrorizes the soft suburban kids.

Mac: Dawg's dad – the bad guy
• Physically he's a picture of the Claremont/Miller Wolverine, cowboy hat, sideburns, and boots. But he's tall and lean.
• Manages a team of illegals for a mid-sized land-scaping business.

Rosa: the heroine
• Poor, beautiful, illegal immigrant, red-head, Latina High School Freshman.
• She's the nanny for Dawg's main victim – James. Dawg has a huge crush on her; she's too old for him, but plays Dawg to save James from beatings.

James: Dawg's favorite victim/ exact opposite of Dawg.
• Tallish, flabby, wealthy, bookish.
• James's parents are materialistic suburban yuppies. They have as little involvement as possible with their son.

BOOK I – SUBURBAN COWBOY

MIDDLE SCHOOL

Dawg: terrorizes the schoolyard, he's fourteen and boss of the 8th grade - extorts lunch money. Roughs up the kids and calls them "bub" and "darlin."

Rosa: high school junior. Very good in math, but struggles in English language classes – refuses to move to a bilingual class.

Class out: Rosa works for James's family. Her job is to take care of James, their 7th grade son, and of course, to do a ton of housework. Rosa saves James from a full-frontal pounding by Dawg, and walks him home from school.

ROSA'S JOB

James does his homework and eats a ton of junk food while Rosa does all the housework.

James gets a playdate – after homework – that's just more junk food and TV with an equally fat friend. Rosa does more work with the Jamaican nanny from next door watching her and telling her to work slower. In this world, the parents have nothing to do with the kids.

Rosa serves dinner to James's family.

She serves and cleans up (eats in the kitchen).

James complains about getting beat up at school and then leaves the table.

Father tells mom to sign the kid up for karate and to call the school . . . then remembers that Dawg's last name is the same as the guy who does their landscaping, Mac – Father will see if Mac's son is the bully.

DAWG'S DINNER - MEET MAC

Dawg cleans the tools and pickup for his dad's landscaping crew. Mac (phone in hand) calls Dawg in and smacks him in the head. Mac drinks

hard and beats Dawg even harder.

SCHOOL IS HELL

Dawg stalks James through the day.
Other kids find this funny.
James tells teacher – she ignores it.

Fight, fight, fight.
Big circle of kids, Dawg pounding James in the middle.
Rosa sweeps in – collars Dawg – he swings – she gets a fat lip, and he stalks away. Kids disperse.

James crying; Rosa comforts him – don't worry little Logan, I'll always be there for you. (In this original treatment, the reveal at the end of this first chapter was that James's last name was Logan. It was later decided the name switch would occur a little differently. In the final version the name switch was done to conceal James's identity from anyone looking for him in ORIGIN #3.)

BOOK II – LIVING IN THE MATERIAL WORLD – TEXAS

James comes home from school all beat up.

Mr. Logan is more concerned that his hired help defied him than with the bumps and bruises on his son and Rosa.

Mr. Logan fires Mac, and gets a couple of neighbors to do the same.

Mac goes away with an apology and a smile. Even tears up the last bill.

James takes a karate class, but he's a wet noodle.

Instructor screams, James cries, that's it for karate.

But James does like Japanese culture and starts reading books on Japan.

Mac gives Dawg another beating and Dawg goes even harder after James.

Nobody talks to James at school. He seems to embrace the loner role.

Mac plans to kidnap James.

Blackmails Rosa – visits her at her shack. Threatens to turn in her whole family. Promises that nobody gets hurt and she gets $1,000.

Sets up simple snatch where Rosa will lead James into Mac's hands.

More Logan Family home life – getting and spending.

Lot of action going on around James – but he is essentially alone.
Rosa goes through with it. Mac snatches James.

Mac to Rosa: for your own good, we have to make it look real. Smacks her hard on the head and knocks her out. Puts the ransom note down her shirt.

BOOK III – OUTTA HERE – TEXAS

Rosa staggers into the Logan's house and hands over the ransom note.

Parents have 24 hours to raise $250,000. Any police, the kid is dead and you are next.

Mr. and Mrs. Logan - We don't have $250,000. We are in debt. House is worth less than we paid. All our money is in the business. We have $5,000 in cash. Rosa hears them.

Mr. Logan puts $5,000 in a briefcase and a gun in his pocket. Will negotiate when the time comes.

Drop off disaster – both Parents killed.

Rosa comes to save James. Confesses to James. Both your parents are dead. I'm getting you out of here.

Mac shows up. Ties up Rosa – upside down. Goes after James.

James pops his first claw - it's a self-defense mechanism that triggers when his life is at stake – kills Mac.

Rosa and Logan have a motorcycle and $5,000. Let's get up to Canada. The further north the better.

PART TWO – CANADA – LUMBER MILL IN THE DEEP WOODS

CANADIAN CHARACTERS

Cookie: The camp cook is James's main tormentor. "I'm sharpening my knife for you."

The Foreman: Young, powerful leader of the camp. No formal schooling, but very smart. Puts James under his brutish protection. (This character will become the basis for Smitty in the final version.)

Victor Creed: Traveling fighter – kicks through small towns and lumber camps, fighting all newcomers for prize money.

The Promoter: Secretly recruiting the Canadian backwoods for Weapon X fighters.

BOOK IV – CALL OF THE WILD – CANADA

The end of the line: Rosa and James run out of luck and money in Canada. Stumble into a riverside sawmill.

The Foreman gives them a chance and some low-paying jobs.

James's workday – splinters and burns.
Kitchen work at breakfast, lunch and dinner.
Hurling scrap wood and bark pulper.

Cookie and the Foreman.
Cookie had been the camp whipping boy, but now he has his own. James tries to keep a low profile, but Cookie constantly torments him. Foreman won't let Cookie go too far. Likes to talk to James. Wants to see him toughen up. Rosa does office work and odd jobs.

James toughens up.

Works hard, the guys accept him.
He's getting buff and strong, and Rosa begins to notice.
Mini-love triangle – Foreman – Rosa – James.

Call of the wild.

James goes hunting to supplement their meager income.
He's a natural hunter. He is also starting to mutate and wants to keep it a secret.

Up against a wolfpack – pops the claw.

Cookie kicks butt. Cookie sees James messed up/tired & hurt – now's the time to attack.

Wolvie will not pop the claws in front of everybody. Cookie cuts James – Foreman breaks it up, but James is badly hurt.

BOOK V – BROKEN HEART – CANADA

James works the heavy machinery in the mill. Lives the lumberman's life. Hard work, hard play.

James becomes a big-time hunter. Brings home rare pelts. Captures wild mink, Rosa starts to raise them.

Rosa and Foreman start to fall in love.

James – out of jealousy/frustration becomes a fighter.
Beats up Cookie – kicks him out of camp.
Gets into bar room brawls and gets a bit of a reputation.

Rosa moves in with Foreman. James moves into the bunks with the guys. Heartbreaker for him, but he takes it like a man.

BOOK VI – CAPTURED – CANADA

Victor Creed finishing off an opponent. Packing up the cage with the promoter. Reveal that the promoter and Creed work for a covert branch of the Canadian Army – Weapon X. They are searching for mutants for the super-soldier program.

The sawmill is in trouble – this part of the wilderness is all but bare. Foreman has to move the mill, but doesn't have the money.

James spends more time in the woods and less at work. Still goes to the bar with the boys. Promoter for a touring cage fight comes to the bar. Introduces "Big Cat" with tall tales and bar talk. $10,000 to any man who can beat him.

Rosa and Foreman – sunny day with James. They have to close the mill and move to the city. They can't afford to move the mill. James is invited, but that's not for him.

Foreman hears about the cage fight – wants a shot at the money. James watches – he has no plans to fight - until he sees what Victor does to people. Cold cocks Foreman and goes into the ring with the champ.

Wolverine fights Sabretooth – wins the $10,000, but has to pop the claw to do it.

James turns money over to Rosa. They will go further north together. But James is captured by Weapon X.

As I'm sure you've noticed by now this compilation of ORIGIN is filled with so much extra stuff that I'm feeling a bit useless at this point. To be quite honest, I'm at a lack for what to write because so much has already been said and said so much better than I could in these few short paragraphs. I mean, I could regale you with funny tales that went even behind-the-scenes of the behind-the-scenes stuff, but then this book would venture off quickly into something more akin to our MAX mature readers imprint than something suitable for the likes of ol' Wolverine.

HURRAYS!

Of course I could use this space to shine a spotlight on the real stars of this book. I mean what can be said about Paul Jenkins, Andy Kubert, Richard Isanove and Comicraft that hasn't already been lavished upon them? Along with Editors Mike Marts and Mike Raicht, they've created not only a new technique in sequential art, but the standard by which all new projects of this era will be measured. What they have created is the first great project of the new comics millennium!

STONES

So, this leads me to a place where I need to either really get to the essence of what this series is all about or stop typing and say, "Thanks, True Believer, for purchasing this book … I hope you enjoyed it!" What did it take to tell this tale? What is really at the core of all this verbiage, ink and paper? It's funny, the one thing that it took for us at Marvel to even consider attempting to write Wolverine's origin is the one ingredient that ol' Wolvie and all our heroes have in spades…

…fearlessness!

It's something that we were really lacking at Marvel at the time, yet it was fearlessness that was the cornerstone upon which Stan Lee, Jack Kirby, Steve Ditko and so many others built the Marvel Universe. As a matter of fact, it had seemed as if every major publisher had become complacent with playing things safe and doing things just because "that's the way they've always been done," even in the face of many a brave creator trying to individually stay the tide of erosion that was eating away at the comics industry. That is until the day Bill Jemas strolled through the door of Marvel.

In my year and a half as Marvel's EIC, I've been continually surprised by Bill's ability to shift gears on the fly, and more importantly, his talent to do so many things. From brilliant business initiatives that have all but saved the comics industry, kept our competition guessing and more importantly, in our rear-view mirror, to being the impetus for stories like the one you've just read.

DISCOVERING THE SECRET

I think the day that everything became perfectly clear to me about Bill was sometime long after the famous meeting in my basement that spawned the idea of Wolverine's origin. I remember Bill walking in with this Marvel strategy card game called "ReCharge." It was just in the process of being designed. All the art looked amazing (as Marvel art always does), so I asked Bill about the game's designers, who they were and how he had found them. Bill's response was as simple as it was shocking, "You're looking at them," he said. That's when the lightbulb went off and all the pieces began to fall into place. All this time I'd been in awe of this tall, lanky, geeky guy who, if not for the bit of salt and pepper around his temples, could pass for an overzealous, hormone-enraged teenager, anxiously awaiting his dateless prom night. How could he be one of the shrewdest business people I've ever met and one of the brightest creators I've ever been around, and also have a talent for designing strategy games? How can he be so proficient at all these things? That's when I discovered Bill's secret. You see, Bill just doesn't know the meaning of the word can't! It's not in the way his brain is wired. Where most of us would sit there and say, "Well, I've never designed a game before, so I really can't do this," Bill just studies a few games and goes about creating one. So, what is it that keeps him from stopping himself before he starts? What's his X-Factor, his mutant ability? Simple, much like our wonderful, hairy, two-dimensional Canucklehead, Bill is the three-dimensional embodiment of his most vaunted trait. He's fearless!

LIKE A BLUNT HAMMER TO MY HEAD

Now that was one very important lesson for me. You see, it brought back all these memories of being a kid and having that fearless nature, that thing inside you that says, "Hey, I can be an astronaut if I want!" That thing that life tends to beat out of us as we get on with it. It's a lesson that I learned to apply to everything I do now at Marvel because I realized I wasn't learning it for the first time. I was just reminded that, much like Wolverine, we all have this trait deep inside of our forgotten past. We all have a "Rose" in our personal ORIGIN that perhaps we've forgotten with the passage of time. For me, my "Rose" came back to me in a flash by Bill's simple ability to not see defeat as an option or even a roadblock.

DEADLINE

Now, as the caption above looms larger and larger with each passing minute, I realize that I better bring this thing to a close and wrap it up with some snappy encapsulation of my overall point! So what are we really talking about here? After you've read all the inside stuff, the behind-the-scenes history, the sketches and the lost plot points, keep in mind that's not really what this project was all about for us. Sure it makes for interesting reading, but the lesson for me, for all of us at Marvel, was not in the pages, but in the doing. We slowly began believing that this project had to be done and then soon enough we realized that we couldn't not do this project. Why? Because we simply didn't know that we couldn't any longer and that is a belief that we have carried with us ever since. It's the trademark of this new Marvel, which you will see, smell, and taste in every new project and idea we come up with. Will we always succeed? Of course not, but as long as we have the incredible support of the world's greatest fans, it will always be and remain "The Marvel Age" of comics!

"Thanks, True Believer, for purchasing this book … I hope you enjoyed it!"

See ya in the funnybooks,

JQ
EEK!
2002

Ever seen one of those daytime soap operas? You remember the part where Chase tells Daphne he's been impregnated with Troy's alien love-baby? I've seen that in real life.

It happened a couple of years ago, back when Joe Quesada had just become the new Editor in Chief of Marvel comics. Joe and I had shared some success working together with Marvel Knights and as a resulat we'd become quite good friends. (Understand, this was in the days before Joe went Hollywood and would actually return his mates' phone calls, but I digress.)

Anyway, Joe asked if I'd be willing to come up to his secret island retreat to participate in his first conference with all of the Marvel Editors – he thought it would be helpful to bring along a comic book writer for everyone to laugh at when discussing creative issues. Actually, Joe was under the mistaken impression I'd had some kind of previous editorial experience. If he'd checked closer, he would have learned that every company I ever did editorial work for has either folded, exploded, or slid into the sea.

Joe's first editorial meeting was very different from those of the previous few years: For a start, no one was fired. Instead of being told what they could not do – a favorite pastime of Marvel Executives in years past—the assembled editors were now being encouraged to come up with bold and interesting new ideas. Enter Marvel president Bill Jemas (who, for those of you who don't know, is the biggest punk in the comic industry). "Is there any reason," asked Bill with a completely straight face, "why we can't do the origin of Wolverine?"

And it is at that moment when thirty-five people looked as though they'd just been informed they were the father of Bill's alien love-baby.

Actually, it's a pretty neat idea when you think about it: a character's mysterious origin can only be shrouded in secrecy for so long before said character begins to look like a twerp. Thirty-five years seemed to be about right for our man Logan. Now that these small pieces of his past have been revealed, I believe it will help reenergize the character in a small way. You may disagree, but this is my section and it's the only chance I get to spout off about character development and to thank the few worthy people below.

First of all, I want to set the record straight: for those people who have speculated on the storytelling involvement of Bill Jemas and Joe Quesada, this story is as much theirs as mine. In fact, Bill and Joe contributed more to the original concept than I did, and this should be recognized. If Marvel Entertainment is a driving force in the comics industry, I'd say we're lucky to have such cool and creative people at the wheel.

I don't have to say much about working with Andy Kubert or Richard Isanove – all you have to do is turn to page one, where you'll find their truly amazing artwork speaks for them.

On a personal note, I will add that Andy's not only an extremely talented chap and a pleasure to work with, but he's also polite enough to listen to me jabbering away for an hour about character motivation without putting the phone down. As you can see, Andy's a brilliant storyteller and I hope he gets all the recognition he deserves for this wonderful piece of work.

Richard Isanove is really a lovely bloke even though he's French. When we embarked on this mission, the idea was to enhance Andy's pencils with painterly techniques that had never been tried, let alone perfected. Richard has managed to do both, and he only attempted formal surrender twice in the entire time he worked on the book.

It is a little known fact that Mike Marts – the editor for this ambitious project – is a nice guy. I say that with the utmost respect in the hopes that he'll finally come clean and admit this to the world. His long-suffering assistant, Mike Raicht, is a good lad, grade one, in my opinion. Thanks, lads for your patience and steady hand.

Finally, some long-overdue thanks to some people who've been very important in my life and career.

To Rick Veitch: thanks for your sage advice and for loaning me your storytelling instincts back in the day. I really appreciate it.

To Kevin Eastman: thanks for giving me my start, helping me along and generally being a great friend. You deserve for your generosity to be returned to you a hundred times over.

To Lou Stathis: I miss you every day, mate. You taught me how to write not just for you but for every editor I'll ever work with.

To Melinda (soon to be Mrs. Jenkins): thanks for putting up with me. You are the most beautiful person in the world.

In fact, the same goes to all of you: Thanks for putting up with me.

Paul Jenkins
Atlanta, 2002

Some of this stuff is gathered together from my conversations with Bill Jemas, Paul Jenkins and some of my own thoughts and ideas about where the story should go. The bulk of my thoughts at the moment focus primarily on the early half of the story and stop somewhere around the time Logan hits the Canadian Outback. I feel that the six issues should be split in two. Three for the early Vanderhurst years and three for the Canadian years. *(Vanderhurst was the new name for the Logan family from Bill J's Texas springboard. Eventually the family name would change to Howlett and the name Logan would come into play a different way.)* Also, please keep in mind that the names I'm using are only for the purpose of getting these bullet points down and done.

The basic action in young Logan's early years takes place in a beautiful estate that I'll call Strathmore for now. *(Eventually to follow suit and become the Howlett Estate.)* The Strathmore Estate and House are built on a mount in the beautiful hills of Asheville, North Carolina. *(This, of course, would later change to Canada.)* The family that built the mansion is the Vanderhursts. The gardener's family name is McMorris but the townsfolk call him Mac for short. *(Mac, in this version, would eventually become the elder gardener Logan, the father of Dawg.)* Mac's son is called Dawg; maybe his real name is Dawson, but because of his weird animal like appearance, everyone's naturally shortened his name. It is very important that Mac and Dawg's appearance and attitude be very similar to how we see Wolvie today. We want the fans to make that instant connection.

The Vanderhurst family made its fortune in ironworks. Old Man Vanderhurst was a tyrant but a completely self-made man with little to no patience for slackers in his life.

Old Man Vanderhurst had several children; the youngest, John, was obviously a child of privilege. John was a kindhearted boy who, though born with a silver spoon in his mouth, always tried to be as generous to those in need as possible. This pissed off the old man to no end.

John became engaged to the lovely Maria Elizabeth Harnegie, another child of means from what seemed to be the ever growing American royalty. *(The name Maria would eventually be dropped and James's mother would be known simply as Elizabeth.)*

The two called upon the greatest architects and designers of the times to build a house from scratch that would rival the castles of ancient Europe. They chose a spot in Asheville, NC to erect their home. *(Early on, the writers and editors were not sure whether or not we were going to make Wolverine a true Canadian or a transplanted one. Eventually, it was agreed that his back-story should stay consistent and that he should be in Canada. It was leaked that he would possibly be American, however, in order to get the fans talking about the book and to stir up some possible controversy.)*

At the bottom of the hill lay a small shantytown made up of Southern ex-slaves and Scot-Irish emigrants, most of whom struggled to make what little they could from working in the nearby coal mines.

John, being the kind of man he was, offered the townspeople a form of on the job training. He would teach them the trades of furniture building, horsemanship, wine making and gardening since these were all trades that would be needed in order to keep Strathmore House running. They were also trades that they then could carry with them wherever they chose to go. This also created less of a rift between the impoverished townfolk and the mega-rich Vanderhurst.

Mac was so adept at learning the art of gardening and horticulture that he eventually became the head groundsman for the estate. His wife died at a young age and left him and his son Dawg behind. Dawg assisted his father on a daily basis. Although Mac was appreciative of the training the Vanderhursts gave him, there was something troubling him, burning at the very pit of his being, and it would always come to a head when he would see the lady of the house.

Old Man Vanderhurst never approved of this mixing of the classes.

After the house's construction Maria gave birth to her and John's first son, Scott, and shortly after, Maria became pregnant with their second son Tiberious. *(The name Tiberious would eventually be switched to James.)*

John took a liking to Dawg, who was by far the youngest worker in his stable. He was surprised that Dawg didn't attend the private school he had created for the townsfolk. Dawg said that his father felt it better he learn a trade.

John imports from England and hires Rose, a beautiful redheaded nanny who bears a striking resemblance to a redhead we all know and love. *(She would eventually come from the town close to the estate.)*

Rose begins her tutoring of Scott; little Ty plays in the same room, too young to care. *(Scott would never actually appear in the book and would only be mentioned as the son who died through the books' first two chapters.)* John occasionally spies Dawg peeking in on Rose and Scott as they run through their studies. John interprets this as maybe the boy has a desire to learn. Dawg, in reality, has the hots for Rose.

Dawg is brought into the house to be tutored along with Scott. John's wife Maria grows attached to Dawg, seeing him as almost another son. Still, at the end of the day, Dawg has to pack up his stuff and travel down the hill.

He tells his father of the lessons he learns and his father decides to teach him one of his own. He beats the boy badly, telling him that no matter how much the people at the top of the hill may pretend to care, he's just a charity case, just like this whole town.

End issue 1. Dawg beaten to a pulp by his old man, his feral blood racing. *(Issue one would eventually start with the arrival of Rose and we would never get to meet the mysterious brother, Scott. We would also only see glimpses of the construction of the Howlett Estate.)*

CLIMBING THE HILL BY JOE QUESADA

The tutoring continues for quite some time. Dawg's only dose of reality comes when the family throws its great Gatsby-like parties that he always has to view from outside the neatly cut shrubs.

Mac's hatred for the family increases. It seems especially directed to John with an always-warm spot for Maria. Sometimes the very sight of her makes him cower and melt.

One day the worst happens. Scott dies of a fever. He is taken from his family at the height of his youth. Maria is inconsolable. From this point on she begins wearing dresses that cover her up to the top of her neck.

Funeral for Scott, with an elaborate casket.

Weeks after the tragedy, Dawg comes to the house to receive his schooling. Maria turns him away. Dawg is a constant reminder of the child she just lost. Mac sees this and his whole demeanor around Maria changes.

Ty is now old enough to begin to study, so he continues with Rose. He too has a schoolboy crush on the young tutor. Dawg, now back to tending the grounds, watches Ty from a distance, jealousy burning in his heart.

Ty misses his brother and gets a dog as a present from his father, who thinks that this will help the boy forget.

Dawg becomes a sort of torturing bully. Whenever little Ty would be playing in the yard, Dawg would scare him by threatening that one day he would cut his heart out.

We see several instances when Dawg corners Ty and scares him until he wets himself. Ty is the epitome of the little rich Lord Fauntleroy. He's meek and weak and will amount to nothing great in the end. Dawg seems to derive tremendous pleasure from watching Ty wet himself.

Ty sees his father get smacked around and berated by Old Man Vanderhurst. He sees his dad get the "You'll never amount to anything" speech. This only makes Ty feel worse about himself. Watching your father get whacked around and take it can do that to a person.

Ty comes to his father's side one day after one of the Old Man's outbursts. They have their first and only man to man talk. They discuss Dawg's bullying. Dad gives advice and a family trinket. This trinket is so important to our story later that it can be changed to fit what we need. I don't care what he gives him as long as it has significance.

Next day, Dawg comes to torture little Ty. Ty won't have any more of it and weakly punches Dawg in the nose. The punch doesn't do a thing but Dawg is so astounded by the affront that he goes ballistic. He grabs Ty's dog and slices its throat!

End of issue 2. Now I want fans thinking what a jerk little Wolvie was.

Ty cries to his daddy and John fires Mac for what his son did. Maria asks John if that wasn't too harsh a punishment, almost taking Mac's side. John gives her a knowing stare, the only

time, in fact, that we've ever seen anything resembling strength of conviction in his eyes in this whole story. Something silent and deep is exchanged between the two.

Later that night Ty tries to comfort his mother. They talk about his brother and all she can keep repeating through her tears is how he was taken from them too soon. Ty leaves the room but just before closing the door behind him he looks back to see his mother unsnapping her long necked dress. He's frozen in the moment not sure whether to turn away in shame or not. The dress slips down slowly to reveal her back and the horrible claw marks she's been hiding. They're obviously not human but made by something far more loathsome.

Mac and Dawg begin to conspire about kidnapping a family member for money. Mac insists it should be Maria; Dawg wants the runt. Mac wins the argument.

The kidnapping is botched. In the melee, John is murdered by Dawg as Mac holds Maria, Rose and Ty at gunpoint. In a childish rage Ty screams "No!" and tries to bull over Mac to get to his dying father. Mac is caught by such surprise and at such a low angle that he never gets to fire the gun properly. It goes off hitting Dawg, who goes flying out of a window out of sight. Ty is buried in Mac's abdomen area, feverishly trying to punch his way through to his father. A surprised look comes across Mac as he collapses to the ground. We see that he's in a puddle of blood and in the distance we see young Ty crying over his father's body with his bloody fists exposing tiny bony claws. This is the moment our readers go "Oh my God!"

As surprised as he is to see these strange things coming out of his hands, nothing is stranger than the sight of his mother cradling Mac's lifeless head in her arms. Sobbing uncontrollably, Maria tells Rose to take Ty away. Run; get out of this miserable place. Run as fast and as far as you can. *(In the final version Wolverine's mother would actually take her own life and would not have a significant role in the rest of the story.)*

End of issue 3

This is what leads us to our adventure in the North Canadian Forest. A couple of random thoughts that were assembled for this sequence. First see some of Bill's notes.

The name Logan comes from the Blackfoot Indians. Much the same way that we have Sasquatch, they have the legend of this Were-Man that they call "The Logan."

Rose takes care of Ty while he learns to be a man in the Canadian Outback. She falls in love with a young man who remarkably resembles Scott Summers. It isn't of course, but it establishes Logan's future addiction for love triangles involving redheads.

Bill had a great idea. Since Wolvie has a healing factor it would only make sense that his brain had a similar ability. We've explained in the past how Weapon X made Wolvie forget all kinds of stuff. Why don't we establish that Wolvie was just as responsible for his own memory loss? For example, if he suffers a trauma that's deep enough, then his brain's healing factor would try to fix that. What's the best way to quickly relieve trauma? Forget that it ever happened!

What I propose is that while Wolvie is becoming Wolvie in Canada; his mother survives and goes to work for a hat factory in NYC. She turns her back on the fortune but always thinks of her poor son, Ty, and where he must be.

The Weapon X program or Team X, whatever they were called, finds out Wolvie's history and for whatever reason that we can think of, needs him to suffer a serious trauma. We'll have to come up with a convincing reason.

They reach out to Maria and tell her that her son has gone AWOL in the Canadian woods. He's become this thing called a Logan. They need her help to reach him.

They tell Wolvie that Dawg is still alive and is coming to finish the job.

We set both pieces in motion. Wolvie attacks in his feral rage and guts the person who he thinks is Dawg.

It's really his mother and Wolvie's brain just fries completely. How do you forget someone who's been with you most of your life? Well, if you had a healing factor you would just forget most of your life.

His mother's last words to him were "He was taken from us."

What I see as the conclusion to our story is flashing forward to today. We see a shadowy figure sniffing around the North Carolina woods. We see an old mansion that has been completely taken over by nature. Vines and decay cover the exterior and the grounds are all but gone.

Of course, it is Wolvie. He holds up the trinket that we set up earlier as something to help bring him to this spot.

He sniffs and sniffs. The claws come out and he begins digging and digging. We see a casket marked "Scott Vanderhurst." Wolvie opens it up and finds it empty. Is his brother dead? What really happened to Scott?

We close the story with Wolvie clawing his way through the vines and growth and entering the mansion. We know that all the answers he seeks will be inside …

… as will a whole host of new questions.

Things left unanswered

Was Mac, Ty and Scott's father?
What happened to Scott? Is he still out there?
What happened to Dawg? Is he dead?

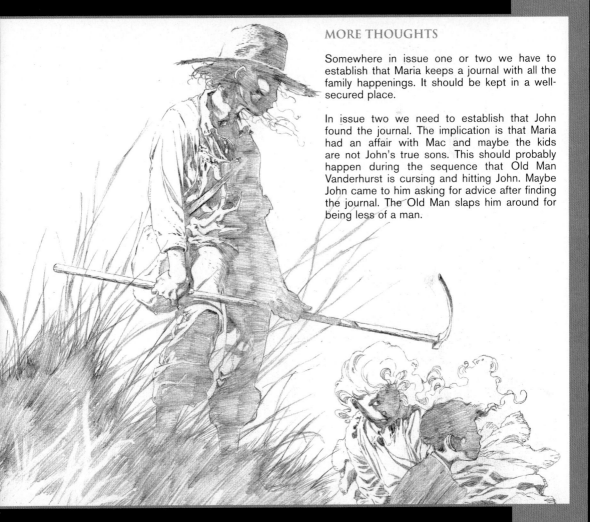

MORE THOUGHTS

Somewhere in issue one or two we have to establish that Maria keeps a journal with all the family happenings. It should be kept in a well-secured place.

In issue two we need to establish that John found the journal. The implication is that Maria had an affair with Mac and maybe the kids are not John's true sons. This should probably happen during the sequence that Old Man Vanderhurst is cursing and hitting John. Maybe John came to him asking for advice after finding the journal. The Old Man slaps him around for being less of a man.

The job seemed an easy one.

When Editor in Chief Joe Quesada walked down the hall to ask us if we'd accept ORIGIN into our office, "yes" blurted out of our mouths before Joe could even finish his sentence. I mean, what else could we say? It was a no-brainer. The schedule had already been set, the freelancers were all chosen and most of the story had already been hammered out. The pieces were all in place. Wolverine's ORIGIN was surely the easiest book an editor could hope for.

At least, that's what we thought at first.

But as the epic storyline contained within this volume proves (not to mention the heaps upon mounds upon loads of supplemental material), ORIGIN was anything but easy. But you won't hear us complaining. Nope. Not when you take a step back and realize just what type of a project ORIGIN really is.

Forget for a minute all the sales hoopla, all the advanced promotion and all the months of preparation. Forget the fact that Marvel's best selling book in over five years topped the charts at #1 for several months in a row. Forget all the hype ... and think about what we've got here. The story readers have been waiting years for. The true history of everybody's favorite X-Man. The ORIGIN of Wolverine!

So who cared if this book was a challenge? It was a welcome challenge.

By the time we got our hands dirty working on the title, Andy Kubert had already finished a dozen character sketches and Paul Jenkins, Bill Jemas and Joe had constructed an extremely tight outline for the first three issues, which explored Logan's early formative years.

What hadn't been resolved yet was what the next three issues would be about. We knew that Logan would experience horrible tragedy at home. We knew that he and his companion Rose would be forced into exile and escape into the Canadian wilderness. But what would happen then? Joe had a few ideas. Paul had a few others. And not to be outdone, Bill had a few of his own, as well.

The trick was throwing everyone's ideas into the proverbial blender and making sure the end result was a concoction everyone would be happy with—Joe, Bill, Paul, Andy, us, and most importantly, the readers. Not an easy trick, mind you, but one we accepted with vigor and enthusiasm. To perform this trick, however, would require hours upon hours of plot meetings, brainstorm sessions, conference calls and emails. Many, many emails.

We saved a few of those email exchanges and we're presenting them here, just to give you a small indication of how big a project Origin became, and how determined we all were to create an extraordinary, one-of-a-kind story for the ages ... like the one you now hold in your hands.

Sit back and enjoy.

Mike Marts
Editor

Mike Raicht
Assistant Editor
2002

From: Quesada, Joe
Sent: Monday, July 30, 2001 9:31 AM
To: Marts, Michael; Jemas, Bill; Raicht, Michael
Subject: Origin #4 Plot

So basically, Logan has some dreams, gets food splattered on him by Cookie, saves some guys in the quarry, dreams some more, desires Rose, dreams some more, sees Rose with Smitty.

This is not exciting enough. Here's how I can validate that statement — I can't think of a cover image that's good enough.

First of all, it should be Cookie that Logan gets his mannerisms from. Cookie says Bub and smokes cigars.

There is little story here and Paul misses a very good moment. He touches on the fact that Logan ages slowly and everyone around him is growing older. We need a scene cut where we see poor Logan mewling about Rose and how much he loves her. We don't realize that time has passed, but from off panel we hear Rose's voice. When we turn the page we get a full page shot of Rose, she's a gorgeous woman and Logan still looks 13.

From: Marts, Michael
Sent: Monday, July 30, 2001 10:51 AM
To: Jemas, Bill; Raicht, Michael; Quesada, Joe
Subject: RE: Origin #4 Plot

I agree with Joe that there seems to be something missing from this story. This issue will end up being a "coming of age" story more than any of the other issues, but I never get a sense that Logan is really becoming a man, at least not in any concrete, physical way.

Maybe this could be improved by making the conflict between Rose/Cookie/Logan even greater. Cookie could be some real slob who lusts after Rose, really laying it on thick with the advances. He taunts the small Logan throughout most of the story and Logan plays the victim. But Logan eventually comes of age and confronts Cookie at a time when Rose is really in danger from the slobbering bastard, and eventually wins, playing the hero. Logan is thrilled at finally standing up to someone and "becoming a man" and figures he's proven himself to the woman he loves ... only to be betrayed by her in Paul's final scene.

JQ: This is very good and a great idea to make significant in the story! I still feel like we need something else.

Also, cut back on the number of dream sequences to one, and probably not start off with it. Maybe it would be better to start off the issue after a couple of years have passed, pick up halfway through Paul's outline and fill in the necessary pieces as we go along.

As for cover image, Joe, what about playing with wolf imagery. Maybe Logan and a wolf on a hill top?

JQ: I'm looking for Wolf reference as we speak!

From: Quesada, Joe
Sent: Monday, July 30, 2001 12:47 PM
To: Jemas, Bill; Marts, Michael; Raicht, Michael
Subject: RE: Origin #4 Plot

Here are a few more ideas. This can make it a better more rounded story.

If we open with a dream sequence it should just be a panel with a close up of 2 burning eyes (wolf eyes but we don't know it yet), just evil and scary! The eyes speak to him in ways only a poofy British writer can figure out ;-). No running with the wolves, just the eyes. When he runs with the Wolves for the first time it should happen for real, not in a dream. Logan wakes up in a cold sweat, scared but also slightly aroused at what's happening to him (remember it's puberty) We make reference to the fact that he's been having these dreams for a while. We'll come back to this.

Cookie tortures poor baby Logan and has the hots for his "sister" Rose.

There is a collapse at the Quarry, 20 men buried alive. It takes them days to dig everyone out and the only survivor is Logan—no one of course can figure it out. Must be the Lord's will. While Logan is buried, Cookie is working on Rose and Smitty is her rescuer but let's not tip our hand to the obvious romance that is happening behind closed doors.

The first time his healing factor is seen by the world is during the fight with Cookie! Remember, Cookie smokes cigars and says "Bub" all the time, Smitty is the Scott Summers metaphor. Logan finds Cookie on the verge of raping Rose and they get into a brawl. Cookie slices a big bloody X on Logan's chest and he sees it heal before his very eyes. This Logan guy wasn't saved by God in the Quarry, he's the Devil's spawn!

Once Logan rescues Rose, Cookie begins his attempt at character defamation, calling Logan a freak and getting everyone in the camp scared. Logan is rejected by everyone he turns to.

He goes to see Smitty or Rose (pick one) to help him and ease his suffering and finds them embracing!

Betrayed he runs into the snowy woods and keeps running losing track of time. He tears at his clothes for no good reason except that it looks cool until he's buck-naked. During this running rage his claws (I like this bit) extract and contract involuntarily, causing all sorts of pain and making for some very cool visuals!

Logan collapses in a circular clearing, on his knees his body steaming from the sweat. He hears a noise and looks around 360 degrees at the woods that surround him. He sees hundreds of the eyes he was seeing in his dreams. Now you can end the issue there or....

He finds a small patch of woods with no glowing eyes and makes a bee-line for it expecting it to be his only clearing and path to safety. He runs desperately but the wolves are following close behind. Soon they catch up and that's when it becomes apparent to the frightened young Logan that they aren't chasing him but following. He is the Alpha Male. This scene ends with a young Logan dissolving into a splash page of an older teenage Logan jumping over snow covered hills followed by his pack. Maybe a deer in the foreground as if they're hunting it. This is all probably better for issue #5 as an opening but I offer it just in case.

So we close issue #4 with the eyes glowing in the woods. Make it only one set.

Issue #5 opens with the eyes coming out of the shadow and it's the biggest wolf you've ever seen!

As it comes out of the woods a million other pair appear in the shadows! The Alpha Male does battle with Logan and he kills it. Next thing we see is the pack come out of the shadows and they lick his wounds clean.

Jump cut to him to him running in the snowy woods by himself, suddenly one wolf is running by him and then more and more and then wee see that they are on the hunt and he's the new king of the jungle!

What do you guys think. Does this work better as a story?

If we agree that there's something here then I'll forward these notes to Paul.

JQ

From: Jemas, Bill
Sent: Tuesday, July 31, 2001 9:02 AM
To: Marts, Michael; Jenkins, Paul; Quesada, Joe
Re: RE: Origin #4 Plot

There really isn't much new in these notes or in the attached outline. I understand Paul's concern with dumping everything but the kitchen sink into these books – so I thought it would be a good idea to lay out the four main priorities that we have been discussing for the past several months.

In that spirit, the attached outline doesn't add much new stuff – but it does re-jigger most of the current scenes into three books with well-defined plots.

Wolverine earned his claws.

THE QUARRY: Logan is a soft kid who has to get tough or die. Based on his abilities and hard work he rises to the top of the heap among the workers – but is constantly undone by treachery.

THE WILD AND THE WOLF PACK: Logan works his way up to leader of the pack – vroom vroom.

Rose carries the guilt in her heart and the story in her diary.

LOGAN'S PAST: she shields him for his own good – and maybe for hers, too.

LOGAN'S LOVE: she treats it like a crush.

TOM is Rose's lover and Logan's father figure – but Logan had to earn Tom's respect. I'm not locked on Mac or Tom, but please not Tad or Todd. (Tom's name is changed to Smitty in the final version of the script.)

Treachery and Enemies

COOKIE wants Logan to replace him on the bottom rung. When Logan gets tough – he can take on Cookie head-on – but Cookie always finds the back door.

DAWG WANTS IT ALL:
Kill Logan to avenge the death of his father.
Take Rose as his wife.
Inherit the Howlett family fortune.
Cookie is nothing compared to this enemy.

Show it – don't say it. This is a big bold graphic action movie.

We are avoiding the basic comic book pratfalls of flashbacks and cryptic references to be revealed later.

The Diary is a great tool for explaining the meaning behind the action – but should not be a substitute for action.

Each comic will have a beginning, middle and end and be readable by someone who hasn't read anything except that comic.

Book Four – Opening Scene

Scrawny, short kid struggles up dirt path carved out of the side of the rock slope.

Knees and elbows scraping – two steps forward, one step back – works his way past a group of diggers with pickaxes and shovels.

Diggers are making fun of Cookie (he's ugly, fat, lazy, etc.).

They take the foreground – and turn up the heat on Cookie – we see the kid in background dump the barrow and turn back down toward the diggers.

Kid slips and barrow rolls out of control with the little dork running after.

Cookie stops the cart – has everybody's attention – including ours because this is now like the Logan/Dawg scene in the first book of the first arc.

Cookie rolls the barrow down the steep side of the hill and sends Logan tumbling down after. The diggers fall over laughing – as we get a close-up of Cookie's smiling, pockmarked face and his yellow rot-toothed grin.

Logan is out in the real world and Cookie makes Dawg look like a ten-year-old bully.

Now we can get to Rose – either in the office with Tom or writing in the diary.

BOOK 4 - SMACKED ALL THE WAY DOWN

Beginning - hitting bottom socially

    Logan and Rose - work for room & board
    Logan stumbling through manual labor
    Rose menial labor in camp office

    Cookie - puts Logan at bottom of the pecking order
    Cookie at the bottom of the camp food chain
    Cookie abuses/degrades Logan - workers love it

    Tom: Rose & Logan are too low to see
    Tom does not help Logan when Cookie attacks
    "Kid, you have to fight your own battles"
    Tom barely knows Rose is alive

Hitting bottom physically

    Winter hardship – near starvation at Quarry
    Cookie steals some of their food ration

    Logan to Rose - don't complain - he'll kill me

Turning the corner

    Logan - the hunter provides food for the camp
    Starts with a couple of rabbits - for Rose
    Hunts - kills deer - feeds the entire camp

Logan - first encounter with the Wolfpack
He sees Wolves - his claws pop on their own
He runs back to Rose - heals along the way

Logan returns to Rose with a hundred questions
Logan to Rose: I don't remember anything
Rose will not tell Logan the truth - he goes to sleep
Rose writes a note to Logan on inside cover of her Diary: she will give the book to him someday he will know all about his past

End - Logan finds his place in the wild

Cookie and Logan II
Cookie uses dirty trick to humiliate and beat up Logan

Tom stops Cookie from killing Logan

Logan and the Wolves I
Pops claws - retracts
Belly up - accepted

BOOK 5 - RISING ALL THE WAY UP

Beginning - Setting up the bad guys

Grandfather dying and repenting
Grandfather talking to mysterious Servant
Wants to give his fortune to James - please find him
James Howlet has fallen off the face of the Earth

Logan - Cookie and the Miners
Logan is boss of the camp - digs like a Wolverine
Cookie madder than ever - secret dirty tricks

Tom - Rose - Logan - love triangle starts

Tom hangs out at their cabin
Tom shows Logan how to use dynamite

Great Times - Logan hits his stride

Logan becomes Tom's right hand man

Logan's nights
Drinks and plays with the workers
Then runs wild with the wolf pack - #2 dog

Rose and Tom start to get romantic at night

Great Treachery

At the mansion - Grandfather's Servant

Finds Rose's letters to housekeeper -letters recap
the Dawg thing - still don't know it's him
Now Servant knows where Rose and Wolvie are

At the Camp - huge cave in
Cookie sabotage - Logan escapes
Logan and Tom - daring rescue - save all but one worker
Logan's arm gets ripped to shreds
Rose bandages fully-healed arm

End - Wolverine: "I am the top dog"

Cookie and Logan III
Cookie is going through dead guy's stuff
Logan blows away Cookie

Rose and Tom tell Logan they are in love

Logan swallows his pride - and goes to the woods

Logan and the Wolves II
Wolverine takes over the pack - "lead dog"

Grandfather to Servant – "Can you find my grandson?"
Servant:"Yes I will Sir, I will be like a hound dawg"
Reveal - Dawg's scarred face mirrors the cover of issue #4

BOOK 6 - DEFEAT - ESCAPE

Beginning - Enter the bad guy
Dawg kills a trapper
They meet outside of the quarry. You're Logan - what a coincidence - there's a Logan in camp
Dawg kills the trapper to keep his secret

Dawg befriends Tom at the canteen
Bumps into Logan - doesn't remember Dawg
They see cage getting set up for prize-fights
Rose and Tom - getting married and getting out

Logan will take over the camp
Tom - needs money and he knows how to get it

Murder #1 - fails

Dawg traps Tom in his cabin
I'm killing you and Howlett - and taking Rose
Tom lights dynamite fuse - drops it between cabin planks
Dawg dives out the front - leaves Tom for dead
Tom dives out the back - knocked out cold

Rose knows
Rose rushes to the cabin - Tom out cold for hours
Tom finally wakes up and he tells her about Dawg
Rose goes to warn Logan

Cage at the canteen
Logan winning big time
Everyone fights hard but fair
Logan exhausted - enter Dawg

Dawg gives Cookie brass knuckles and $50
Logan wins - but is battered and tired

End: Dawg ambushes Logan

Rose tries to break up the fight
Logan accidentally kills her

Dawg "saw it all" - Logan is a monster/killer

Logan runs for the woods

Logan and the Wolves III
Wolverine runs wild in the woods

Cookie burns the diary

Being asked to work on one of the most exciting comic projects in recent memory was enough of a jolt to me. I was floored when I got the call. I remember that time so vividly.

So you can imagine the angst that I felt when I read the first script, and talked with Paul at length as to how to interpret his (along with Joe and Bill's) ideas of what these characters should look and act like. Paul and I had a few long, in-depth conversations that helped to put me at ease. Paul is an excellent storyteller; like when you're in grade school and the teacher is reading a book to you, showing the pictures at the same time. Except I saw the pictures in my mind as he was talking. I saw exactly how these characters should look and act.

After the initial conversation about the characters, I immediately set out to get all the reference for the costumes and clothing for that time period at my library. I had also found a few books at a bookstore. I spent a great deal of time sifting through all the reference that I had acquired, trying to piece together the characters that I had envisioned with the costumes. I love going through reference, thumbing through the old books and reading about the items and time period that I am referencing. Reading about the things that I will be drawing really helps me to reach the right frame of mind for when I set out to do the storytelling.

These are the thoughts that we had as we were putting together the characters. And a few ideas that I had thrown in there myself…

Andy Kubert

Andy Kubert
2002

ROSE

ROSE

A sweet little Irish girl. We wanted her to have red hair and make her very innocent. I tried to give her a refined, yet attractive look. But she was going to go through some tough times, and she had to look as though she could take it. I'm very happy with the way she turned out. Even as she aged throughout the series, I thought she worked well.

LITTLE JAMES

James was to be thin, sickly looking. He wasn't supposed to look anything like Logan looks today which I thought was a great idea. He was also supposed to be a spoiled little rich kid. I thought of Alfalfa from "The Little Rascals" when I envisioned his look. And the dress costume, which was actually worn by wealthy boys from that time period, really helped get his soft demeanor across.

'JAMES'

DAWG

Dawg was a snot-nosed little punk with ripped clothes and hair that was never combed. He was a total bully. A trouble-maker. There were a few kids around my neighborhood when I was a kid that always picked on the skinny, weaker kids. They all kind of gelled into one look, having the same kind of turned up nose and squinty eyes, like they were looking for a fight. And for me, that look turned into Dawg.

'DAWG'

- HAIR THAT LOOKS LIKE IT WAS CUT WITH GARDENING SHEARS.
- FRECKLES
- SCRAPPY-LOOKING
- DRESS IN OVERALLS?
- ROPE BELT
- NO SHOES?

THOMAS LOGAN

He was easy. Thomas was to look like a crusty Wolverine. I picked the clothing from a book I had bought which had old pictures of miners and poor people in it. The beard style was also perfect for this time period. I enjoyed drawing Thomas. Too bad he didn't make it past the second issue.

SIDE
BURNS
TOO
PERFECT

'JOHN'

JOHN HOWLETT

John was to have a kind, gentle demeanor about him. But when he got mad, you knew he meant business. Clean shaven, always impeccably dressed. I pictured him as a young Jimmy Stewart. Again, the costume and hairstyle were taken from old reference book photographs.

OLD MAN HOWLETT

This guy was to be one of the surly types; old, yet feisty. I thought a bit of Ebeneezer Scrooge when I was drawing him, even with his costuming. I love the beard and moustaches that were in style back then. He was another of my favorites to draw.

ELIZABETH HOWLETT

This woman needed to have the look of a woman with a lot of skeletons in her closet. I thought she should be pale and very sickly looking, usually dressed in black. To me, this sketch makes her look a bit like an alien. I kinda liked that.

'ELIZABETH'

MARTHA

MARTHA

Martha was the housekeeper. I guess I watch too much TV, but I was thinking of a typical television housekeeper as I put this together. I thought she should be a bit pudgy, with hair piled high. She was to be very faithful, and I think this came across in her look.

KENNETH

Kenneth was the stable-master, and I saw him as John's right-hand man for any job that came up. I saw him as a big, burly type of guy; one you would like to pal around with, or go out to the pub and have a few pints with.

Kenneth

STEP 1: THE LINE ART
After scanning a quickly painted canvas, apply the drawing onto it.

STEP 2: SPOTTING THE BLACK
Establish the darkest shadows.

STEP 3 AND 4: RENDERING
Start to blend the lights and darks to create the impression of volume and texture.

STEP 5: THE REFLECTION
Flip the result and paste it, replacing the black by a dark brown to make the figures less tangible.

Step 6: Fine-Tuning

This takes longer than all the other steps combined. Lighten up certain areas and darken others to separate background from foreground; add highlights to accentuate the volumes and create the water effect; fade the remaining line art into the "painting".

ORIGIN #1 COVER PENCILS

ORIGIN #2 COVER PENCILS

ORIGIN #3 COVER PENCILS

ORIGIN #4 COVER PENCILS

ORIGIN #6 COVER PENCILS

ORIGIN #1 PENCILS

ORIGIN #2, PAGE 1 PENCILS

ORIGIN #2 PENCILS

ORIGIN #4, PAGES 15 & 26-28

ORIGIN #5, PAGES 2-3

ORIGIN #6, PAGES 20-22 & 25